HOW THINGS WORK
INSTRUCTIONS

1 Open the front flap on the VR viewer. Bring the top and side flaps up and over. The side flaps attach to the side of the viewer with Velcro.

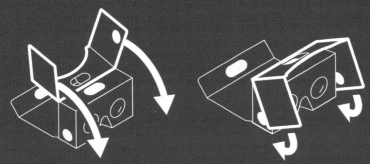

2 Download PI VR How Things Work, available on the App Store or Google Play. Direct links to the store locations are found at: pilbooks.com/PIVRHowThingsWork.

3 Launch the app. You may be asked to calibrate your viewer by scanning the QR code found on the bottom of the viewer itself. You will be able to change your viewer settings later in the options menu.

4 After calibrating your viewer, you will be prompted to scan the QR code found to the right to verify your possession of this book.

5 You will see a double image of the virtual environment on your phone. Insert your smartphone into the front compartment of the VR viewer. The line between the two images should line up with the notch at the center point of the viewer, between the two lenses. If your screen seems blurry, make sure the smartphone is aligned precisely with the center of the viewer. Adjusting the phone left or right a few millimeters can make a big difference. The tilt of the viewer and the phone can also affect how the screen looks to you.

6 Look around to explore! PI VR How Things Work does not require a lever or remote control. You control each interaction with your gaze. When you see a loading circle, keep your gaze focused until it loads fully to access videos, slideshows, and games.

Loading

7 Gaze at the X to close out of video, slideshow, or game screens.

Exit

pi
Publications International, Ltd.

Get the App!

This book is enhanced by an app that can be downloaded from the App Store or Google Play*. Apps are available to download at no cost. Once you've downloaded the app to your smartphone**, use the QR code found on page 1 of this book to access an immersive, 360˚ virtual reality environment. Then slide the phone into the VR viewer and you're ready to go.

Compatible Operating Systems

- Android 4.1 (JellyBean) or later

- iOS 8.0 or later

Compatible Phones

The app is designed to work with smartphones with a screen size of up to 6 inches. Removing your device from its case may provide a better fit in the viewer. If your smartphone meets the above operating system requirements and has gyroscope functionality it should support GoogleVR. Publications International, Ltd. has developed and tested this software with the following devices:

- Google Nexus 5, Google Nexus 5X

- Motorola Moto Z

- Apple iPhone 6, Apple iPhone 6 Plus, Apple iPhone 7, Apple iPhone 8, Apple iPhone X

- Samsung Galaxy S6, Samsung Galaxy S6 Edge, Samsung Galaxy S7, Samsung Galaxy S8

Caution

The viewer should not be exposed to moisture or extreme temperatures. The viewer is not water resistant. It is potentially combustible if the lenses are left facing a strong light source.

Cover art from Shutterstock.com.

Interior art from Encyclopædia Britannica, Inc., Library of Congress, Prints and Photographs Division, and Shutterstock.com.

App content from Encyclopædia Britannica, Inc., Filament Games, and Shutterstock.com.

 Publications International, Ltd.

For inquiries email: customer_service@pubint.com

ISBN: 978-1-64030-326-3

Manufactured in China.

8 7 6 5 4 3 2 1

*We reserve the right to terminate the apps.
**Smartphone not included. Standard data rates may apply to download. Once downloaded, the app does not use data or require Wi-Fi access.

CONTENTS

INTRODUCTION

Physics is one of the major branches of science. People who work in physics are called physicists. Physicists study matter and the forces (pushes or pulls) that act on it. Matter is what makes up all physical objects. Physicists also study many different forms of energy. The objects that physicists study range in size from the tiny building blocks of matter to huge groups of stars. In this book, we will look at how things work, from matter to forms of energy to machines.

FIVE FAST FACTS

① Without the science of physics, we could not possibly bridge the Hudson River or the Golden Gate much less build a jet plane, use a cell phone, or watch a television show.

② All other natural sciences depend upon physics for the foundations of their knowledge.

③ One major branch of physics, mechanics, deals with the states of matter—solids, liquids, and gases—and with their motions.

④ Some branches of physics are based on the different kinds of energy that interact with matter. They deal with electricity and magnetism, heat, light, and sound.

⑤ Physics is closely related to engineering. Engineers often employ physical principles in solving everyday problems.

USE THE VR VIEWER AND ASSOCIATED APP

Enhance your experience by using the app! Put your smartphone in the VR viewer to see simple machines in action!

ATOMS

The tiny units of matter known as atoms are the basic building blocks of chemistry, the study of matter and the chemical changes that matter undergoes. An atom is the smallest unit of matter that has the characteristic properties of a chemical element, such as hydrogen, oxygen, calcium, iron, gold, and neon. More than 90 types of atom exist in nature, and each one forms a different element. Atoms also join together chemically to form molecules.

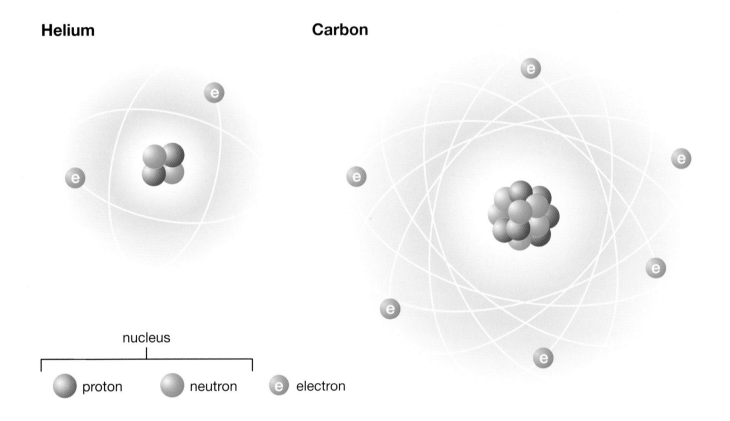

Helium

Carbon

nucleus

proton   neutron   e electron

FOUR FAST FACTS

1. All atoms are roughly the same size.

2. About 50 million atoms of solid matter lined up in a row would measure only 0.4 inch (1 centimeter).

3. Since the end of the 19th century, it has been known that atoms are themselves made up of smaller particles.

4. It requires a great deal of energy to break an atom into its component parts.

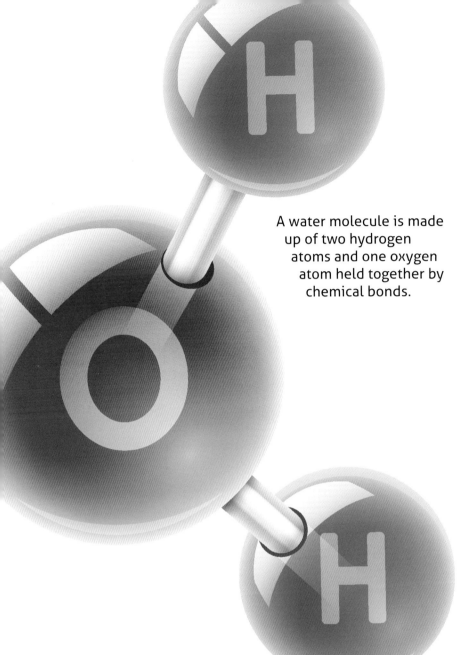

A water molecule is made up of two hydrogen atoms and one oxygen atom held together by chemical bonds.

PARTS OF AN ATOM

Atoms are made up of three basic types of particle: protons, neutrons, and electrons. These particles (as well as other particles smaller than atoms) are known as subatomic particles.

Most of an atom consists of empty space. Its mass is concentrated in its center, which is called the nucleus. The nucleus consists of protons and neutrons. Protons have a positive electrical charge, while neutrons are electrically neutral—they carry no charge. Overall, then, the nucleus has a positive charge.

Circling the nucleus is a cloud of electrons, which are negatively charged.

IONS

Ordinarily, an atom has the same number of electrons and protons, each with an electrical charge of the same size. The negatively charged electrons and positively charged protons thus cancel each other out overall, so the atom as a whole is electrically neutral. Sometimes, however, an atom gains or loses electrons. It then becomes either negatively or positively charged and is called an ion.

Neon.

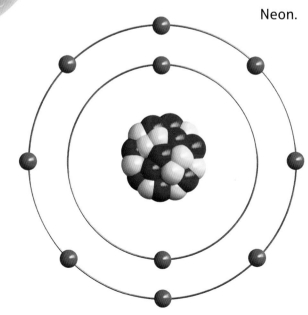

● **10 Protons** ○ **10 Neutrons** ● **10 Electrons**

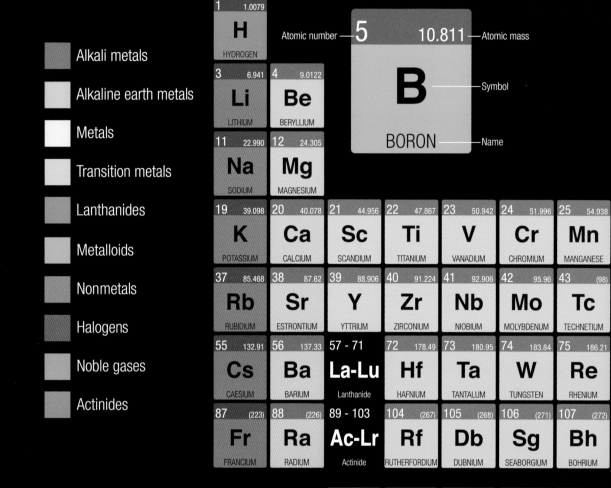

Legend

- Alkali metals
- Alkaline earth metals
- Metals
- Transition metals
- Lanthanides
- Metalloids
- Nonmetals
- Halogens
- Noble gases
- Actinides

Atomic number — 5
10.811 — Atomic mass

B — Symbol

BORON — Name

1 1.0079 **H** HYDROGEN						
3 6.941 **Li** LITHIUM	4 9.0122 **Be** BERYLLIUM					
11 22.990 **Na** SODIUM	12 24.305 **Mg** MAGNESIUM					
19 39.098 **K** POTASSIUM	20 40.078 **Ca** CALCIUM	21 44.956 **Sc** SCANDIUM	22 47.867 **Ti** TITANIUM	23 50.942 **V** VANADIUM	24 51.996 **Cr** CHROMIUM	25 54.938 **Mn** MANGANESE
37 85.468 **Rb** RUBIDIUM	38 87.62 **Sr** ESTRONTIUM	39 88.906 **Y** YTTRIUM	40 91.224 **Zr** ZIRCONIUM	41 92.906 **Nb** NIOBIUM	42 95.96 **Mo** MOLYBDENUM	43 (98) **Tc** TECHNETIUM
55 132.91 **Cs** CAESIUM	56 137.33 **Ba** BARIUM	57 - 71 **La-Lu** Lanthanide	72 178.49 **Hf** HAFNIUM	73 180.95 **Ta** TANTALUM	74 183.84 **W** TUNGSTEN	75 186.21 **Re** RHENIUM
87 (223) **Fr** FRANCIUM	88 (226) **Ra** RADIUM	89 - 103 **Ac-Lr** Actinide	104 (267) **Rf** RUTHERFORDIUM	105 (268) **Db** DUBNIUM	106 (271) **Sg** SEABORGIUM	107 (272) **Bh** BOHRIUM

57 138.91 **La** LANTHANIUM	58 140.12 **Ce** CERIUM	59 140.91 **Pr** PRASEODYMIUM	60 144.24 **Nd** NEODYMIUM	61 (145) **Pm** PROMETHIUM
89 (227) **Ac** ACTINIUM	90 232.04 **Th** THORIUM	91 231.04 **Pa** PROTACTINIUM	92 238.03 **U** URANIUM	93 (237) **Np** NEPTUNIUM

ELEMENTS

Any substance that cannot be decomposed into simpler substances by ordinary chemical processes is defined as a chemical element. Only 94 such substances are known to exist in nature (and two of them occur in only trace amounts). They are found either chemically free, such as the oxygen in air, or combined with other elements, such as the hydrogen and oxygen in water. Two dozen additional elements have been produced in the laboratory through the techniques of nuclear physics.

NAMES AND SYMBOLS

Each element has a symbol that is used by chemists around the world as a kind of shorthand. Symbols for elements may have one letter or two. Wherever possible, the symbol is the first letter of the common name or the Latin name of the element. For example, the symbol for hydrogen is H; for carbon, C; for uranium, U. The symbol for potassium is K, after *kalium*, the Latin name for that element. Since there are not enough single letters to go around and several elements may start with the same letter, other letters must sometimes be added. For example, helium is He and chlorine is Cl.

THE PERIODIC TABLE

In 1869 the Russian scientist Dmitry Mendeleyev organized the elements in a table on the basis of their physical and chemical properties. The periodic table, as it came to be called, is an important tool for scientists in many fields.

					2 4.0026 **He** HELIUM
5 10.811 **B** BORON	**6** 12.011 **C** CARBON	**7** 14.007 **N** NITROGEN	**8** 15.999 **O** OXYGEN	**9** 18.998 **F** FLUORINE	**10** 20.180 **Ne** NEON
13 26.982 **Al** ALUMINIUM	**14** 28.086 **Si** SILICON	**15** 30.974 **P** PHOSPHORUS	**16** 32.065 **S** SULFUR	**17** 35.543 **Cl** CHLORINE	**18** 39.948 **Ar** ARGON

25 54.938 **Mn** MANGANESE	**26** 55.845 **Fe** IRON	**27** 58.933 **Co** COBALT	**28** 58.693 **Ni** NICKEL	**29** 63.546 **Cu** COPPER	**30** 65.38 **Zn** ZINC	**31** 69.723 **Ga** GALLIUM	**32** 72.64 **Ge** GERMANIUM	**33** 74.922 **As** ARSENIC	**34** 78.96 **Se** SELENIUM	**35** 79.904 **Br** BROMINE	**36** 83.798 **Kr** KRYPTON
43 (98) **Tc** TECHNETIUM	**44** 101.07 **Ru** RUTHENIUM	**45** 102.91 **Rh** RHODIUM	**46** 106.42 **Pd** PALLADIUM	**47** 107.87 **Ag** SILVER	**48** 112.41 **Cd** CADMIUM	**49** 114.82 **In** INDIUM	**50** 118.71 **Sn** TIN	**51** 121.76 **Sb** ANTIMONY	**52** 127.60 **Te** TELLURIUM	**53** 126.90 **I** IODINE	**54** 131.29 **Xe** XENON
75 186.21 **Re** RHENIUM	**76** 190.23 **Os** OSMIUM	**77** 192.22 **Ir** IRIDIUM	**78** 195.08 **Pt** PLATINUM	**79** 196.97 **Au** GOLD	**80** 200.59 **Hg** MERCURY	**81** 204.38 **Tl** THALLIUM	**82** 207.20 **Pb** LEAD	**83** 208.98 **Bi** BISMUTH	**84** (209) **Po** POLONIUM	**85** (210) **At** ASTATINE	**86** (222) **Rn** RADON
107 (272) **Bh** BOHRIUM	**108** (277) **Hs** HASSIUM	**109** (276) **Mt** MEITNERIUM	**110** (281) **Ds** DARMSTADTIUM	**111** (280) **Rg** ROENTGENIUM	**112** (285) **Cn** COPERNICIUM	**113** (284) **Nh** NIHONIUM	**114** (289) **Fl** FLEROVIUM	**115** (288) **Mc** MOSCOVIUM	**116** (292) **Lv** LIVERMORIUM	**117** (294) **Ts** TENNESSINE	**118** (294) **Og** OGANESSON

61 (145) **Pm** PROMETHIUM	**62** 150.36 **Sm** SAMARIUM	**63** 151.96 **Eu** EUROPIUM	**64** 157.25 **Gd** GADOLINIUM	**65** 158.93 **Tb** TERBIUM	**66** 162.50 **Dy** DYSPROSIUM	**67** 164.93 **Ho** HOLMIUM	**68** 167.26 **Er** ERBIUM	**69** 168.93 **Tm** THULIUM	**70** 173.05 **Yb** YTTERBIUM	**71** 174.97 **Lu** LUTETIUM
93 (237) **Np** NEPTUNIUM	**94** (244) **Pu** PLUTONIUM	**95** (243) **Am** AMERICIUM	**96** (247) **Cm** CURIUM	**97** (247) **Bk** BERKELIUM	**98** (251) **Cf** CALIFORNIUM	**99** (252) **Es** EINSTEINIUM	**100** (257) **Fm** FERMIUM	**101** (258) **Md** MENDELEVIUM	**102** (259) **No** NOBELIUM	**103** (262) **Lr** LAWRENCIUM

ATOMIC NUMBERS

The heart of each atom, its nucleus, contains one or more protons, each having a positive electric charge. The number of protons, and thus the number of positive charges, ranges from one in hydrogen, the lightest element, to 92 in uranium, the heaviest element that occurs naturally in significant amounts. The number of protons in an atom is called its atomic number.

The Latin name for the element lead is *plumbum*, and its symbol is Pb.

DANGER **LEAD HAZARD** WORK AREA KEEP OUT NO SMOKING, EATING, OR DRINKING

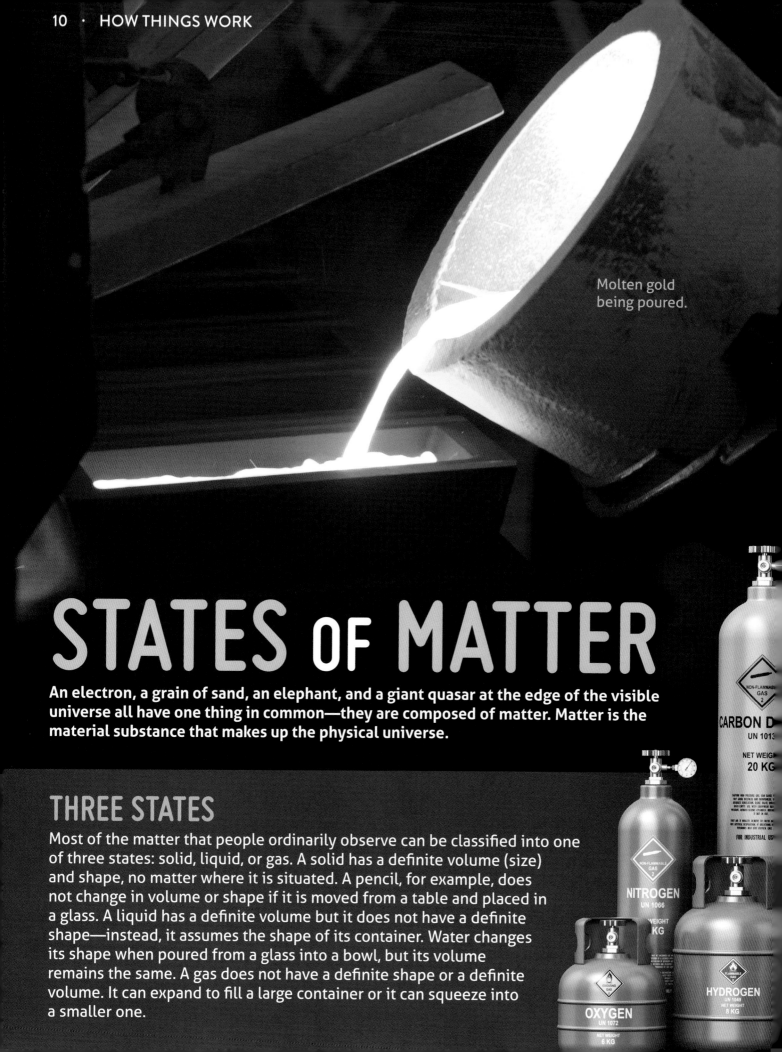

Molten gold being poured.

STATES OF MATTER

An electron, a grain of sand, an elephant, and a giant quasar at the edge of the visible universe all have one thing in common—they are composed of matter. Matter is the material substance that makes up the physical universe.

THREE STATES

Most of the matter that people ordinarily observe can be classified into one of three states: solid, liquid, or gas. A solid has a definite volume (size) and shape, no matter where it is situated. A pencil, for example, does not change in volume or shape if it is moved from a table and placed in a glass. A liquid has a definite volume but it does not have a definite shape—instead, it assumes the shape of its container. Water changes its shape when poured from a glass into a bowl, but its volume remains the same. A gas does not have a definite shape or a definite volume. It can expand to fill a large container or it can squeeze into a smaller one.

CHANGES OF STATE

At a given temperature and pressure, a substance will be in the solid, liquid, or gaseous state. But if the temperature or the pressure changes, its state may also change.

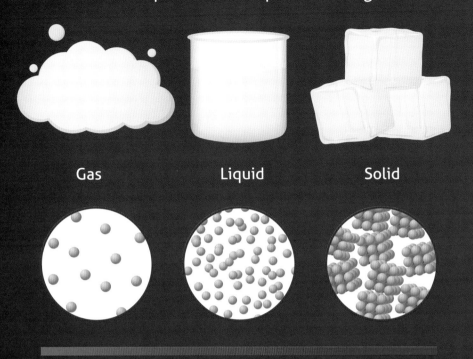

Gas   Liquid   Solid

Ice is water in the solid state. If it is removed from a freezer and placed in a warm pan, the ice melts and changes to its liquid state—water. If the pan is then placed on a hot stove, the water eventually boils and changes to water vapor—the gaseous state of water.

PLASMA

At extremely high temperatures atoms may collide with such force that electrons are knocked free from the nuclei. The resulting mixture of free negative and positive particles is not a gas according to the usual definition. Such material is called a plasma. Some scientists consider the plasma state to be a fourth state of matter. Plasma exists in and around the stars and throughout interstellar space.

Gas in containers.

Potential energy.

ENERGY

Energy is one of the most basic fields of science. All activity in the universe can be explained in terms of energy and matter. But the definition of energy is not at all simple since energy occurs in many different forms, and it is not always easy to tell how these forms are related to one another and what they have in common. One of the best-known definitions of energy is the classical definition used in physics: Energy is the ability to do work.

WHAT IS WORK?

In physics, work is done when a force applied to an object moves it some distance in the direction of the force. If a person pushes a sofa across a floor, she exerts a force to push the sofa over a given distance—the distance from the starting point to the end point. The amount of work she does is equal to the force she exerted multiplied by the distance the sofa was pushed.

FORMS OF ENERGY

Energy exists in many different forms. Electrical energy is associated with the tiny units called atoms that make up everything in the universe. The energy is created when particles called electrons move from one atom to another. Heat and light are also forms of energy. One form of energy can also be transformed into another. When a light is turned on, the electric energy in the lightbulb changes to light and heat.

POTENTIAL VS. KINETIC ENERGY

Each form of energy can be described as either potential energy or kinetic energy. Potential energy is stored energy. It is the energy an object has because of its position, and therefore its ability, or potential, to move. Kinetic energy is the energy of motion. An arrow stretched back on a bowstring has potential energy. If the string is let go, it moves forward and pushes the arrow through the air. As the arrow moves, it gains kinetic energy. When it comes to rest, however, it loses kinetic energy and gains potential energy.

Kinetic energy.

TYPES OF ENERGY

MECHANICAL ENERGY

Mechanical energy is all the energy that an object has because of its motion (kinetic energy) and its position (potential energy). Machines use mechanical energy to do work. For instance, a hammer uses mechanical energy to drive a nail into a board. When the hammer is raised, it has potential energy from the work done in lifting it. When the hammer is moved toward the nail, the potential energy becomes kinetic energy, which can do the work of driving the nail into the board. When the hammer hits the nail, energy is transferred to the nail and then to the board.

LIGHT ENERGY

Light energy is sometimes called radiant energy. Visible light is the only kind of radiant energy that can be seen by the naked eye. Radiant energy is carried by electromagnetic radiation. Other examples of radiant energy are radio waves, microwaves, X-rays, and gamma rays.

SOUND ENERGY

Sound energy is produced by the back-and-forth motion of a vibrating object. This motion produces sound waves that travel away from the object and toward a receiver, such as a human ear.

THERMAL ENERGY

All substances are made up of molecules, which are always moving around randomly within a substance. Thermal energy is the total kinetic energy of all of the molecules in a substance. Thermal energy is not the same thing as heat, though the two terms are related. Heat is the amount of thermal energy transferred between objects of different temperatures.

CHEMICAL ENERGY

Chemical energy is the energy that is stored in the bonds between atoms and molecules. Chemical energy is what holds the atoms in a molecule together. It also is what holds molecules in a substance together.

ELECTRICAL ENERGY

Electrical energy results from the flow of electrons and protons through an object or substance, or between two such entities. Electrical energy can be seen in nature in a bolt of lightning, which consists of a large number of electrons flowing through air all at once.

NUCLEAR ENERGY

Nuclear energy is the energy that is released by splitting an atom, a process known as fission. Nuclear energy can also be released by joining two nuclei together to form a single nucleus. The latter process is called fusion.

Nuclear power plant.

Baking bread involves chemical reactions.

CHEMICAL REACTIONS

A chemical reaction is a process in which one or more substances are converted to one or more different substances. In the reaction, the atoms of the starting substances are rearranged, forming new substances that have different properties. The number of atoms and the amount of mass are the same before and after the reaction takes place; thus mass is conserved. Chemical reactions are important in both nonliving and living systems. The reactions involve the transfer, transformation, and conservation of energy.

PRODUCTS, REACTANTS, AND ENERGY

The substances in a chemical reaction may be chemical elements, molecules, or compounds. The substances present at the start of a chemical reaction are called the reactants; the substances formed by the reaction are called the products.

Energy plays a key role in chemical processes. In a chemical reaction, chemical bonds are broken in the reactants and new chemical bonds are formed in the products. Breaking bonds requires energy, whereas forming bonds allows energy to be released.

The formation of rust is a chemical reaction.

Photosynthesis is a chemical reaction.

EXAMPLES OF CHEMICAL REACTIONS

Burning fuels, smelting iron, and baking bread are just some of the human activities incorporating chemical reactions.

Chemical reactions in the digestive system help break down food into glucose and other constituent molecules that can be absorbed by cells.

Perhaps the most important of all chemical reactions is photosynthesis, which directly and indirectly supports almost every living thing on Earth. In photosynthesis, plants, algae, and certain microorganisms transform light energy from the Sun into the chemical energy of food.

SOUND

Every kind of sound is produced by vibration. The sound source may be a violin, an automobile horn, or a barking dog. Whatever it is, some part of it is vibrating while it is producing sound. The vibrations from the source disturb the air in such a way that sound waves are produced. These waves travel out in all directions, expanding in balloonlike fashion from the source of the sound. If the waves happen to reach someone's ear, they set up vibrations that are perceived as sound.

THE SPEED OF SOUND

Sound waves travel at a constant speed, regardless of the loudness or softness of a sound. Temperature, however, does affect their speed. At room temperature (70° F, or 22.2° C) sound travels in air at a speed of 1,129 feet (344 meters) per second. With each rise of one degree Fahrenheit, the speed increases by more than one foot per second. Air pressure has little or no effect. Humidity has a slight effect, the speed of sound being somewhat greater in humid air than in dry air. Since 1,129 feet is about one fifth of a mile, sound waves travel one mile in about five seconds (or one kilometer in about three seconds).

The sides of a megaphone hold sound waves in and allow them to escape in only one direction, thus intensifying the waves.

CONDUCTORS OF SOUND

Many other substances are better conductors of sound than air. Like all gases, air is a poor medium for sound waves. Liquids, such as water, are better; and rigid solid substances, such as iron and stone, are best of all. Sound waves travel in much the same way in liquids and solids as in air.

When sound waves strike a flat, hard, smooth surface, they bounce back, creating an echo.

LIGHT

One of the most familiar and important forms of energy is light. Many scientists believe that millions of years ago light from the Sun triggered the chemical reactions that led to the development of life on Earth. Without light the living things now on Earth would be unable to survive.

THE VISIBLE RANGE

Humans see light in what is called the visible range. It includes all the colors beginning with red and continuing through orange, yellow, green, blue, indigo, and violet. Some people can see farther into the violet region or the red region than other people.

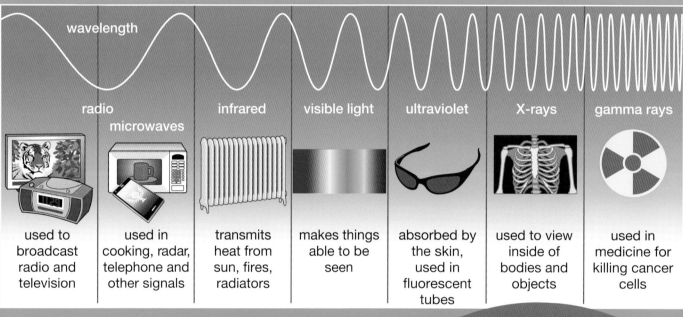

radio / microwaves	infrared	visible light	ultraviolet	X-rays	gamma rays
used to broadcast radio and television	used in cooking, radar, telephone and other signals	transmits heat from sun, fires, radiators	makes things able to be seen	absorbed by the skin, used in fluorescent tubes	used to view inside of bodies and objects	used in medicine for killing cancer cells

wavelength

Pit viper.

WHAT CAN ANIMALS SEE?

Some animals have a different sensory range than humans. Pit vipers, for example, have sense organs (pits) that "see" rays that humans feel as heat. These rays are called infrared radiation. Bees, on the other hand, not only see some of the colors that humans see but also are sensitive to ultraviolet radiation, which is beyond the range visible to humans.

ELECTROMAGNETIC RADIATION

Instruments have been built that can detect and photograph objects by means of infrared rays or ultraviolet rays. X-rays, which also can be used to photograph objects, are yet another form of light. Scientists have learned that all these forms of energy and many other kinds of energy, such as radio waves, microwaves, and gamma rays, have the same structure. They all consist of electrical and magnetic fields that work together in a special way to form electromagnetic radiation.

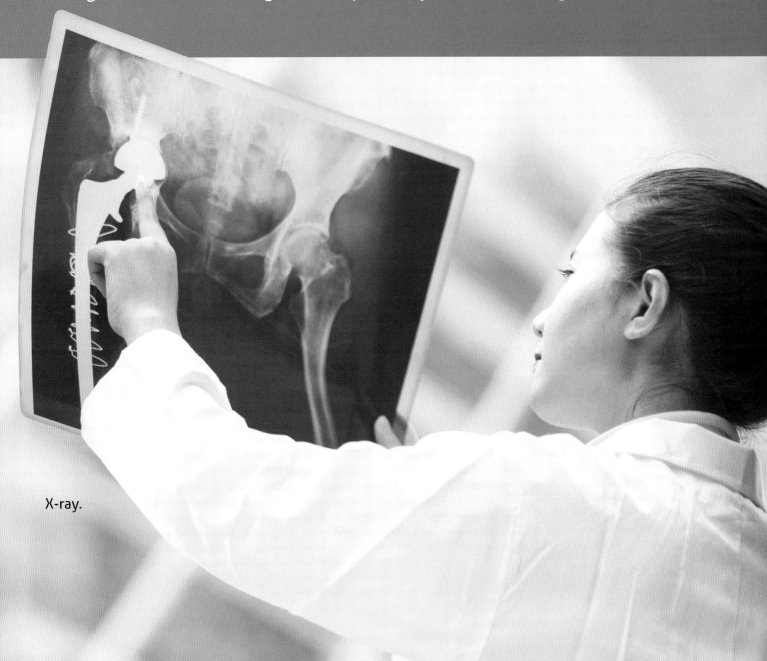

X-ray.

WAVELENGTHS

Scientists use a unit of measurement called wavelength to describe light waves. Like waves moving across a pool of water, light waves have peaks and valleys. The distance between two of these peaks is its wavelength. The color of light depends on its wavelength. Red light has the longest wavelength. Violet light has the shortest wavelength.

FIRE

In 1783, the great French chemist Antoine Lavoisier solved what was the most significant chemical problem of the day by demonstrating the connection between oxygen and fire. By brilliant experiments and delicate measurements, Lavoisier showed that burning, or combustion, consisted of the union of oxygen with other materials. Because this union, called oxidation, is one of the most important chemical processes, his discovery started the development of modern chemistry.

Antoine Lavoisier.

IGNITION POINT

The degree of temperature at which a substance will catch fire and continue to burn is called its ignition point or its kindling point. A substance that can be ignited in the air is said to be flammable (or inflammable).

TEMPERATURE

After a fire has started, it will be self-supporting only when the temperature created by the combustion of the burning substance is as high or higher than its ignition point. This is one of the most important laws of fire. Some very hard woods, such as ebony, require a great deal of heat to burn. If the end of a stick of ebony is placed in a coal fire, it will burn. When it is drawn out, the fire of the smoldering ebony itself is lower in temperature than the ignition point of the wood. The flames thus will die.

FLAMMABLE
KEEP FIRE AWAY

ELECTRICITY

Electricity results from the movement or accumulation of negatively charged electrons in relation to positively charged protons. Electricity can be seen in nature in a bolt of lightning. Lightning is composed of a large number of electrons flowing through air all at once, releasing a huge amount of energy. Scientists have learned how to generate, or create, electricity. This is useful because electricity that is generated can be controlled and sent through wires. It can then power such things as heaters, light bulbs, and computers. Today, electricity provides most of the energy to run the modern world.

Power plant.

GENERATING ELECTRICITY

The electricity used for lighting, heating, and running appliances is made by machines called generators located at power plants. The generators cause a current to flow by moving a magnet past a coil of wire, which pushes electrons through the wires of the coil. Wires carrying the current travel to houses and other buildings. More wires connect to the power outlets in rooms. When a person plugs in an iron or another electric device, the current travels into the device. The current then makes the device work. A chemical reaction in a battery can also produce an electric current.

FIVE FAST FACTS

1 The ancient Greeks were the first to study electric forces.

2 In the American colonies during the 1700s, Benjamin Franklin proved that lightning is a form of electricity.

3 Electrical forces are responsible for holding body cells together in the shape they have. In fact, electrical forces are fundamental in holding all matter together.

4 As printed words are being read, electrical currents speed along nerve cells from eye to brain.

5 Alessandro Volta, an Italian professor, devised the first battery in 1800.

Alessandro Volta.

Portable generator.

MAGNETISM

In ancient times men knew of a special kind of rock that could pull other rocks of the same kind and pieces of iron toward itself. Such rocks were called lodestones. In modern times man uses the same force exerted by the ancient lodestones to generate electric power, to store information in computers, and to study the secrets of the universe. The force is called magnetism, and objects that exert it are known as magnets. By the end of the 19th century, all the elements were known to have some magnetic property.

MAGNETISM IN NATURE

Certain rocks and minerals are magnetic in their natural state. Materials which retain their magnetism independently of their surroundings are called hard, or permanent, magnets. Magnetic forces always exist between permanent magnets. In addition, permanent magnets exert forces on certain other materials, such as iron, which by themselves do not act magnetic.

Earth itself is a large but weak magnet.

Iron is a soft magnet.

SOFT MAGNETS

Materials which can be attracted to magnets but which are not themselves permanent magnets are called soft, or temporary, magnets. This distinguishes them from nonmagnetic substances such as wood. Soft magnets can be magnetic and can act like magnets only when they are in the presence of a permanent magnet. Some soft magnets such as iron can be made into hard magnets. One way is to roll or hammer a hot piece of the soft magnet into a needle shape and then to place it next to a hard magnet as it cools.

ELECTRONS

Magnetism happens when electrons behave in a certain way. The electrons spin around the atom's nucleus and form tiny magnetic forces. Sometimes many of the electrons in an object spin in the same direction. In these cases, all the tiny magnetic forces from the electrons add up to make the object one big magnet.

Credits cards have a magnetic strip.

SIMPLE MACHINES

A machine is a device that does a physical task. Some machines make moving or lifting things easier. Other machines carry people from place to place. Yet other machines help in building or making things. The most basic machines are called simple machines. They are the inclined plane, the wedge, the lever, the wheel and axle, the screw, and the pulley. Simple machines change the strength or direction of a force, such as a push or pull.

An inclined plane is a flat surface that is raised at one end. It takes less force to move an object up along an inclined plane than it does to lift it straight up.

Ramps and sloping roads are examples of inclined planes.

A wedge is a piece of material that narrows to a thin edge. Pushing the wedge in one direction creates a force in a sideways direction.

The head of an ax is a wedge. Swinging the ax into a log can split the log apart.

A hammer acts as a lever when used to pry a nail from a board. The part of the hammer that rests on the board is the fulcrum.

A lever is a bar or board that rests on a support called a fulcrum. A lever can transfer and increase the force applied to one end of it. People use levers to move heavy objects or to pry things loose.

An axle is a shaft, or rod, that is fixed to the center of a wheel. A steering wheel in a car is a wheel-and-axle machine.

SEE SIMPLE MACHINES IN ACTION IN THE VR VIEWER!

A doorknob is a wheel that turns an inner shaft (axle) that moves the latch.

Turning a screw produces a force that can push the screw into wood or tighten it against a nut.

By pulling down on one end of a rope, a person can lift an object attached to the other end.

A screw is a thin rod with edges, or threads, that curve around it.

A pulley is a wheel with a rope or something similar around its edge. The pulley changes the direction of the force applied to one end of the rope.

POTTERY

Pottery is the art of making containers, sculptures, and other objects of clay. The clay is shaped and then fired to harden it. The items created in this way also are called pottery.

TYPES OF POTTERY

There are three basic types of pottery—earthenware, stoneware, and porcelain. Earthenware is the simplest and oldest form of pottery. Stoneware is very hard. Porcelain is smooth, light, and thin, and usually light can shine through it. Both stoneware and porcelain originated in China more than 1,000 years ago.

METHODS OF MAKING POTTERY

One of the simplest ways to make pottery is with long ropes of clay. The potter coils these ropes on top of each other to make a bowl or vase shape. Then the potter smooths the surface.

In another method, called slip casting, the potter pours liquid clay into a mold. The clay then hardens into the desired shape. Slip casting is useful for making pottery in flat or unusual shapes.

Porcelain.

These women work with a potter's wheel.

Kiln.

A POTTER'S WHEEL

Pottery is often made on a potter's wheel—a round, flat surface that spins around. The potter puts a chunk of clay on the wheel and then shapes the spinning clay into a pot or other rounded object. Because the wheel spins, it is easy for the potter to keep the sides even.

KILNS

When the pottery is completely dry, it is ready to be fired. The potter places it in a kiln, or high-temperature oven. Earthenware may need a temperature of 1,400° F (760° C), while stoneware or porcelain may need 2,700° F (1,480° C).

These pots have been glazed.

GLAZING AND PAINTING

After firing, the hardened pottery can be glazed and painted. Glazes are made of ground minerals that produce different colors. Paint may be applied either under or over the glaze. After glazing and painting, the pottery is often fired again so that the glaze hardens and becomes shiny.

GLASS

A glassblower at work.

Glass is a material made by cooling molten ingredients such as silica sand fast enough so that no visible crystals form. Since glass has no sharp melting point, most types can be shaped while hot. The finished glass is usually hard, brittle, and transparent or translucent.

THE ADVANTAGES OF GLASS

- Glass is extremely durable.
- Most glass products can be made cheaply.
- The raw materials of glass are abundant and easily obtained. Mass-production methods turn them into such products as bottles or lightbulbs at a very low cost.
- Many kinds of glass can be made to suit particular purposes.
- Glass does not retain odors. It is nonporous—that is, liquids cannot seep through—and can be completely sterilized.

HOW GLASS IS MADE

The main ingredient for glass is pure silica, or sand. It takes very high temperatures to make glass from sand. Adding certain chemicals to the silica decreases the amount of heat needed for the process. Chemicals can also make the glass stronger or add colors to it.

The silica and chemicals are called the batch. To begin, glassmakers add to the batch some glass that has already been made. This scrap glass helps the silica to melt.

Once the batch is melted, glassmakers remove any bubbles or streaks. Then the melted glass can be molded into shapes or rolled into sheets and allowed to harden.

GLASSBLOWING

Modern machines can quickly and easily create huge numbers of glass items. But artists still create unique items through a method called glassblowing. Glassblowers blow air through a tube into melted glass to create different shapes.

Bottles at a glass factory.

IRON AND STEEL

Modern life depends greatly on iron, the most widely used of all metals. It is needed to carry out even the simplest daily tasks. Steel, an alloy (mixture) of iron and carbon, is nearly always helping to do the job. The concrete in highways and in towering buildings needs steel for added strength. Transportation relies on these metals, whether in the form of an iron horseshoe or as a special steel alloy in a vehicle sent into outer space. A complete list of all the uses for iron and steel would seem endless, and new uses are found each year.

IRON ORES

Iron is one of the most widespread elements on the Earth. It makes up approximately 5 percent of the Earth's crust. Much of this iron is found in such small concentrations in other rocks, however, that it cannot be used economically for mining. The ores used in making iron and steel are iron oxides, which are compounds of iron and oxygen. There are several important types of iron-oxide ores. The most plentiful is hematite. Others are limonite, also called brown ore, and magnetite, a black ore. Magnetite, which is named for its magnetic property, has the highest iron content.

People mine iron ore at this open pit mine.

Hematite is an iron-oxide ore.

Steel is used in the construction process.

This furnace helps turn cast iron into steel.

STEEL

Steel is an alloy of iron and carbon in which the carbon content ranges up to 2 percent. Steels can be divided in two main grades: carbon steels and alloy steels. Carbon steels generally include those in which carbon has the dominant influence on the properties. Carbon steels contain three principal elements—iron, carbon, and manganese. They are classified as low-, medium-, or high-carbon steels.

Alloy steels are made by adding to carbon steels enough of one or more other substances—such as nickel, chromium, or molybdenum—to change the character of the metal.

Modern printing press.

THE
PRINTING PRESS

Few single inventions have had such far-reaching consequences as the printing press, a machine by which images are transferred to paper by means of ink. Before its invention, most books were copied out individually by hand, a time-consuming process. Books were rare and so expensive that only the very wealthy could afford them. The printing press allowed books and other texts to be produced quickly, accurately, less expensively, and in large numbers. This led to a revolution in communications.

Page from the Gutenberg Bible.

Illustration of Johannes Gutenberg.

THE GUTENBERG BIBLE

The German craftsman Johannes Gutenberg is widely credited with the development of the first printing press. The printing press could not have been developed, however, without paper and movable type—individual pieces of type that can be reused again and again. The letters or other characters of movable type can be arranged into words, sentences, and paragraphs and can later be rearranged to print different words. Both paper and movable type were invented in China. Printing was first mechanized in Germany. About 1455 Gutenberg used a printing press and movable type to print his masterpiece, a three-volume Bible now known as the Gutenberg Bible.

THE EARLY PRINTING PRESS

The early printing press was an adaptation of the medieval screw press used to make paper. The paper press was in turn modeled after the ancient wine-and-olive press of the Mediterranean area. In the early printing presses, the movable type was arranged and fixed in place over a flat wooden plate called the lower platen. Ink was applied to the type, and a sheet of paper was laid on top. To operate the press, a long handle was used to turn a heavy wooden screw, which exerted downward pressure against an upper platen. The upper and lower platens pressed the paper and type together like a vise. The press produced sharp images on the paper. This kind of wooden printing press could print about 250 sheets per hour, on one side of the paper.

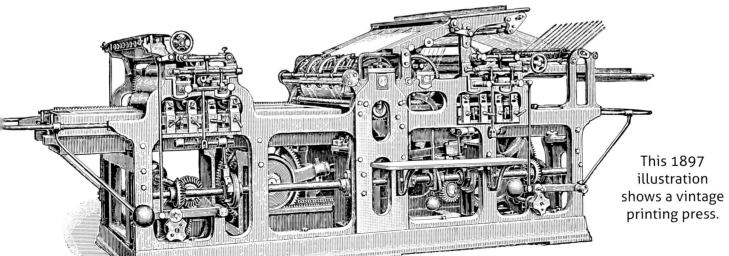

This 1897 illustration shows a vintage printing press.

TELESCOPES

A telescope is an instrument that allows people to see distant objects. Telescopes are important tools in astronomy. There are several different types of telescopes. Some, called light telescopes, gather light from objects. Other telescopes gather different kinds of information about the object being viewed.

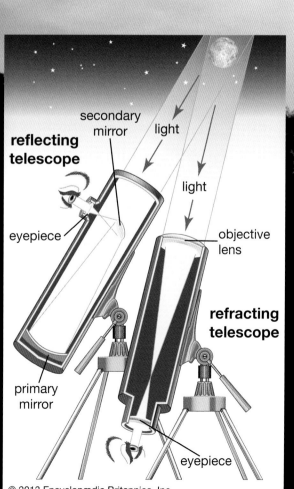

reflecting telescope

secondary mirror

light

light

eyepiece

objective lens

refracting telescope

primary mirror

eyepiece

© 2013 Encyclopædia Britannica, Inc.

REFRACTING VS. REFLECTING

There are two basic types of light telescopes: refracting telescopes and reflecting telescopes. A refracting telescope uses lenses. A lens is a curved piece of glass that refracts, or bends, light. A reflecting telescope uses mirrors. Some telescopes use both lenses and mirrors.

REFRACTING TELESCOPES

A refracting telescope is a tube with one or more lenses at each end. Light from a far-off object enters the far end of the tube. The lens or lenses at that end, called objective lenses, bend the light. They focus it at a point near the other end of the tube. The light forms an image, or picture of the object, at this point. The lens or lenses at this end, called the eyepiece, magnify the image.

REFLECTING TELESCOPES

Reflecting telescopes are much more powerful than refracting telescopes. A reflecting telescope has a curved mirror at the bottom of the tube. Light from an object reflects, or bounces, off the mirror. The mirror focuses the light at a point in the tube. A second mirror sits in the way of this focused light. It sends the light out the side of the tube, through an eyepiece. A lens in the eyepiece magnifies the image formed by the light.

These radio telescopes are found in New Mexico.

GATHERING INFORMATION

Some types of telescopes do not collect light. These telescopes collect other forms of energy from space—for example, radio waves, infrared radiation, and X-rays. Radio telescopes look like huge bowls. They collect radio waves that travel to Earth's surface. Infrared, X-ray, and other similar telescopes are mounted on spacecraft.

MICROSCOPES

Many objects too small to be seen with the unaided eye can be viewed through a microscope, an instrument that produces magnified images of such objects. The development of the microscope greatly affected human life. Before it was invented, little was known about tiny organisms such as bacteria and protozoa.

A scientist prepares a slide to be seen under a microscope.

USES

Today the microscope is used in many capacities. Microbiologists, for example, use the microscope to study cell structures and the cell processes that are responsible for life itself. Specialized low-power microscopes, called stereoscopic binocular microscopes, are used in the assembly of small electronic circuits and for detailed surgical operations. As an industrial tool, the microscope assists in the detection of food spoilage, drug adulteration, and minute structural defects in metals.

OPTICAL MICROSCOPES

There are several types of microscopes. Optical microscopes, also called light microscopes, work like magnifying glasses and use lenses. The object to be studied sits under a lens. As light passes from the object through the lens, the lens makes the object look bigger.

THE COMPOUND MICROSCOPE

One type of optical microscope is a compound microscope. In a compound microscope a lens near the object makes a larger image of the object. This lens is called an objective lens. Another lens, known as the eyepiece, bends the light again. As a result, the eyepiece forms an even bigger image of the image made by the objective lens.

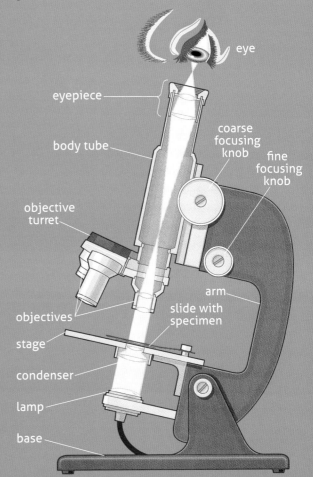

eye

eyepiece

body tube

coarse focusing knob

fine focusing knob

objective turret

objectives

slide with specimen

stage

arm

condenser

lamp

base

Electron microscope.

ELECTRON MICROSCOPES

To view small objects even more closely, scientists use electron microscopes. These microscopes use beams of electrons instead of light to magnify objects. Electron beams cannot travel far in air. Objects must be put in a vacuum, or airless space, before they can be seen with an electron microscope. Electron microscopes can magnify objects up to 1 million times. However, they cannot be used to study living things because living things cannot survive in a vacuum.

CAMERAS

A camera is an instrument used to record pictures of people and objects. The word *camera* comes from the Latin words *camera obscura*, which mean "dark chamber," since the earliest experiments with capturing images took place in a darkened chamber.

TRADITIONAL CAMERAS

A traditional camera is a lightproof box with an opening at one end where light can be admitted and a device at the other end to hold film. The opening that controls the light is called the aperture, and the part that opens and closes the aperture is called the shutter. The shutter controls the length of time that light is admitted to the camera.

The earliest camera was the camera obscura, which was used to view eclipses of the sun. People stood in a small, dark room that had only a tiny hole to let in light. An upside-down image of the scene outside appeared on the wall across from the hole.

TAKING A PICTURE

During the process of taking a picture, light from a person or object passes into the camera through one or more lenses. The lenses focus the light onto the film stored in the camera. The chemically coated film reacts to the light and records an image of the object. Photographers can then remove the film from the camera and use special chemicals to make prints of the image on paper.

Louis-Jacques-Mandé Daguerre formed pictures called daguerreotypes in the 1830s.

DIGITAL CAMERAS

A digital camera works in a similar way as a traditional camera, but instead of using film, it captures the image on an electronic chip. The chip is a light sensor that turns the image into electric signals. Most digital cameras have a small screen that displays the image right away. The camera can also store the image on a memory card.

ELECTRIC LIGHTS

Modern living was greatly enhanced with the invention of the electric lightbulb in the late ninteenth century. It allowed people to see at night with equipment that was much safer than the kerosene lamps, commonly used for street lighting.

ELECTRIC POWER

With electric power, light is produced in two main ways. In the common incandescent lamp, current is forced through a fine metal filament that has a high resistance. The energy used in overcoming this resistance produces a white heat, and the filament glows brilliantly. In another type of lamp, called an electric discharge lamp, an electric current excites a gas until it emits light.

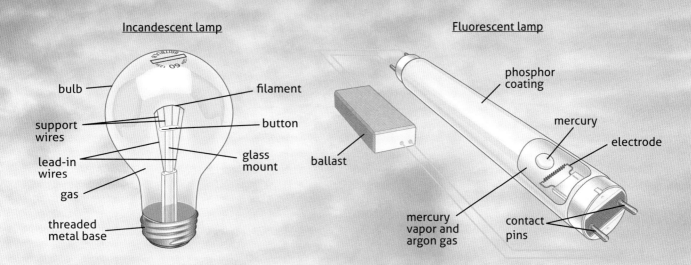

Incandescent lamp

bulb — filament

support wires — button

lead-in wires — glass mount

gas

threaded metal base

Fluorescent lamp

phosphor coating

mercury

electrode

ballast

mercury vapor and argon gas — contact pins

INCANDESCENT LAMPS

Modern lamps and lighting began with the invention of the incandescent electric lamp, commonly called a lightbulb. In 1860 the English physicist Joseph W. Swan developed a primitive incandescent lamp, one that used a filament of carbonized paper in an evacuated glass bulb—that is, a bulb from which the air has been removed to create a partial vacuum. The vacuum was necessary because otherwise the oxygen in air would burn up the hot filament. Lack of a good vacuum and an adequate electric source, however, resulted in a short lifetime for the bulb and inefficient light.

THE MODERN LIGHT BULB

Swan's design was substantially the same as the one used by Thomas Alva Edison of the United States nearly 20 years later. In 1880, after the improvement of vacuum techniques, both Swan in England and Edison in the United States independently produced a practical lightbulb. They each enclosed a carbon filament in a glass bulb, pumped out the air, and then sealed the bulb where the glass had been left open for the pumping. Edison has received most of the credit for the invention because he also developed the power lines and other equipment needed to integrate the incandescent lamp into a practical lighting system.

Thomas Edison.

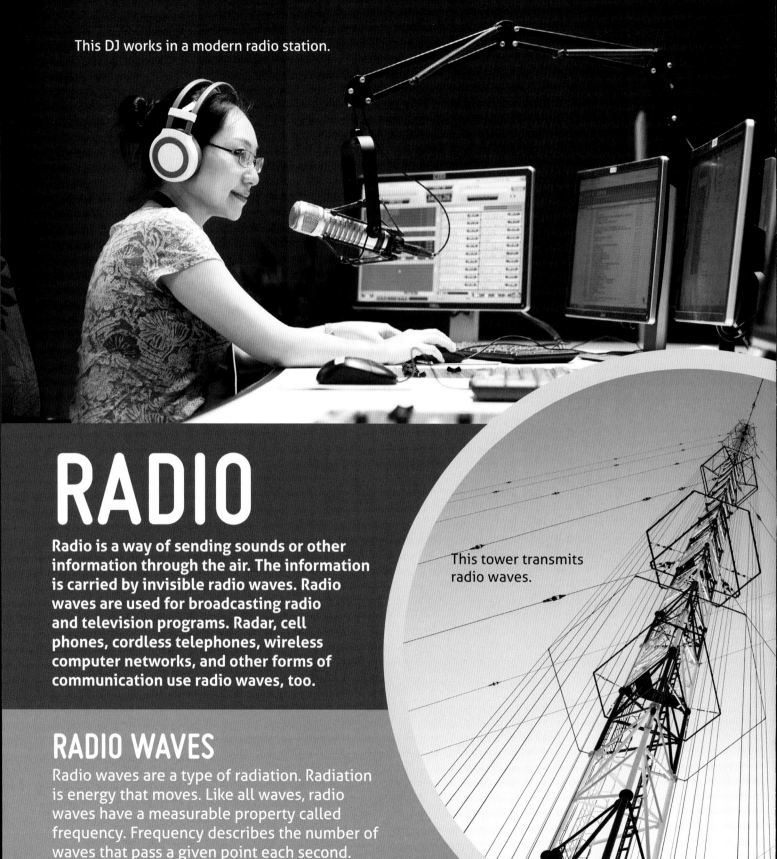

This DJ works in a modern radio station.

RADIO

Radio is a way of sending sounds or other information through the air. The information is carried by invisible radio waves. Radio waves are used for broadcasting radio and television programs. Radar, cell phones, cordless telephones, wireless computer networks, and other forms of communication use radio waves, too.

This tower transmits radio waves.

RADIO WAVES

Radio waves are a type of radiation. Radiation is energy that moves. Like all waves, radio waves have a measurable property called frequency. Frequency describes the number of waves that pass a given point each second.

TRANSMITTERS

Radio waves are sent out, or emitted, by a device called a transmitter. The transmitter turns talking, music, pictures, or other information into electric signals. The transmitter combines these electric signals with radio waves of a certain frequency. The waves spread out in all directions from an antenna connected to the transmitter.

Vintage radio.

RECEIVERS

Radio waves are picked up by an antenna connected to a device called a receiver. The receiver separates the electric signals from the radio waves. Then it turns the electric signal back into the original sounds or pictures. A receiver that picks up waves that carry sound is called a radio. A radio sends the electric signal through speakers so the sound can be heard. Each radio station sends out radio waves of a certain frequency. A person changes a radio from one frequency to another to hear different stations. The frequency thereby serves as the radio station channel.

SATELLITE RADIO

Instead of using antennas on the ground, satellite radio stations send broadcasts from satellites. Satellite radio stations provided crisp, clear sound. They also can be heard over a much wider area than traditional radio stations.

INTERNAL-COMBUSTION ENGINE

When a fuel is burned in air, the resulting hot gas tries to expand, generating a force that can be used to move a piston in a cylinder, as in the automobile engine, or to drive the blades of a turbine. In either case, because combustion takes place within it, the engine is called an internal-combustion engine.

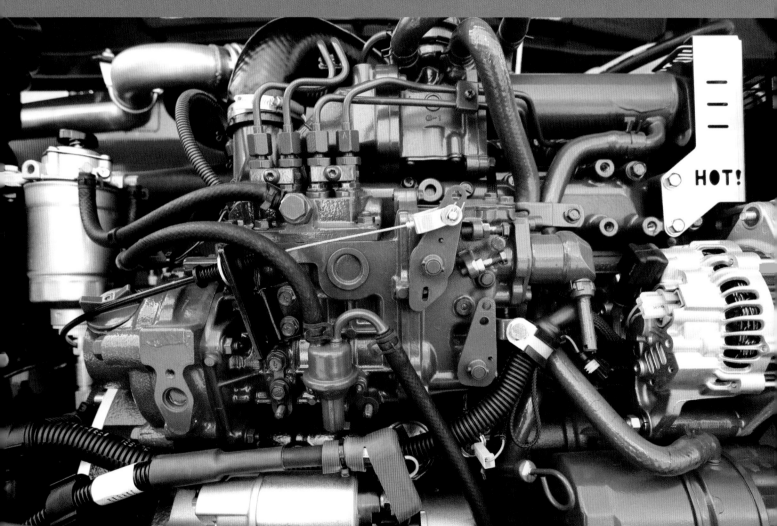

HOT!

GASOLINE VS. DIESEL

The two most common internal-combustion engines are the gasoline and the diesel engines. The first is used in most automobiles. The diesel engine burns a heavier fuel and finds its primary application in larger vehicles such as ships, locomotives, heavy trucks, and buses, though it is also used in some automobiles. Almost any liquid or gaseous fuel, however, can be used in an internal-combustion engine, including gasoline-alcohol mixtures called gasohol, alcohol, methane gas, and compressed coal gas.

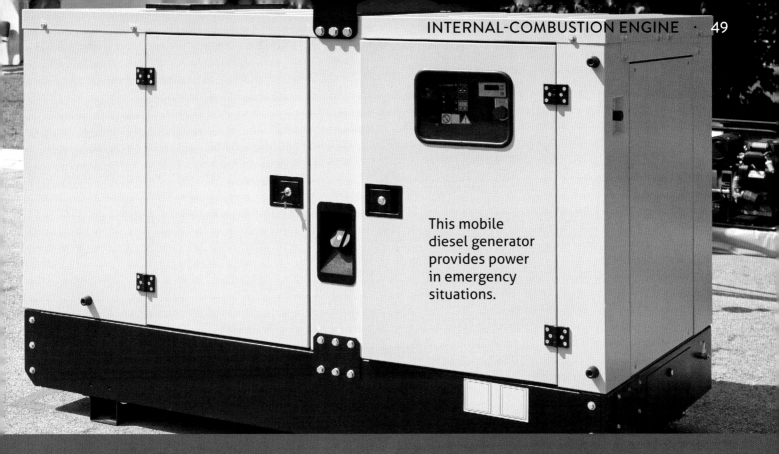

This mobile diesel generator provides power in emergency situations.

FOUR FAST FACTS

1 The German engineer Nikolaus A. Otto developed the modern four-stroke cycle engine in 1876, which—coupled with the invention in 1885 of the carburetor by another German, Gottlieb Daimler—ushered in the automobile age.

2 Seeking improved engine efficiencies, the German engineer Rudolf C.K. Diesel developed in 1892 the engine that bears his name.

3 All internal-combustion engines must be started with an auxiliary device that can be either a starting motor or, for large diesels, compressed air.

4 Only a fraction of the energy of the fuel is converted to useful power. Most of the energy becomes heat that must be removed by a cooling system.

This German stamp shows Rudolf Diesel.

REFRIGERATION

The cooling of substances or enclosed spaces to low temperatures is called refrigeration. Refrigeration is used most often to keep foods or medicines from spoiling, since bacterial growth is slowed at lower temperatures. A common example is the home refrigerator, in which foods can be stored for days at temperatures of around 40° F (4° C). Foods kept frozen at temperatures near 0° F (−18° C) can be stored for months without decay or loss of flavor.

MECHANICAL-VAPOR COMPRESSION

Most household refrigerators and freezers use a method of refrigeration called vapor compression. A fluid called the refrigerant is recirculated through a so-called closed cycle. In commonly used mechanical refrigeration systems, there are four basic components: a compressor, a condenser, an expansion valve, and an evaporator. In home refrigerators the evaporator section is the food compartment and its surrounding coils, which contain the refrigerant. The vapor leaving the evaporator section is compressed. The compressed gas is then condensed into a liquid by the condenser, which transfers heat to the external surroundings through coils at the back or bottom of the refrigerator. The liquid is then passed through an expansion valve and fed back into the cold-chamber evaporator, where it absorbs heat as it is vaporized.

VAPOR-COMPRESSION REFRIGERATION

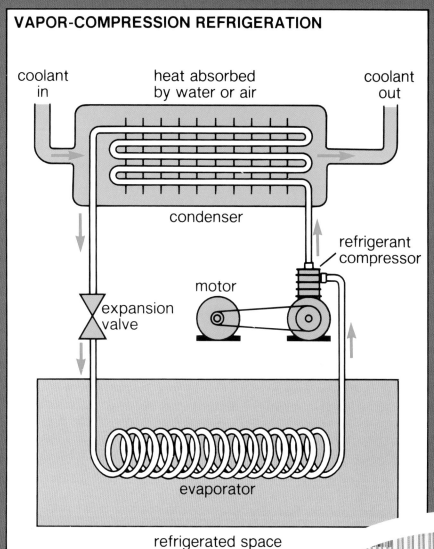

coolant in

heat absorbed by water or air

coolant out

condenser

refrigerant compressor

expansion valve

motor

evaporator

refrigerated space

A RUNNING REFRIGERATOR

For a continuously running refrigerator, a steady cold state is reached when the heat leaking into the unit just equals the heat absorbed by the refrigerant. In practice, however, most refrigerators work only intermittently. If the temperature in the food compartment slightly exceeds the desired temperature, a thermostat activates the compressor motor and the compartment is cooled to just below the required temperature. The compressor is then shut off, to be restarted when the compartment warms up.

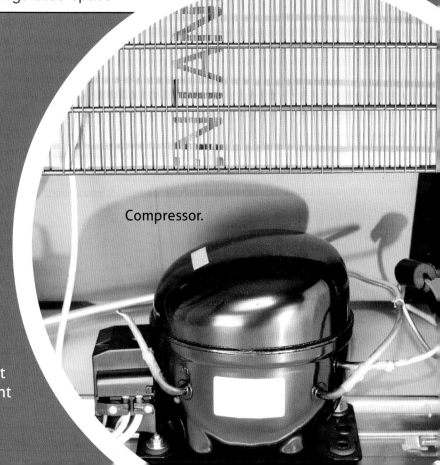

Compressor.

This 3-D printer creates an object from plastic.

PLASTICS

Among the most versatile materials ever developed, plastics can be made to resemble and even replace such diverse materials as metal, wood, glass, china, stone, cloth, rubber, jewels, glue, cardboard, varnish, and leather. The word plastic comes from the Greek *plastikos*, meaning "moldable" or "formable." When heated to a liquid or semisolid form, plastics can be molded into almost any desired shape; when cool they harden into a solid.

MAKING PLASTICS

Most plastics are made from chemicals that come from petroleum, natural gas, or coal. Heating these chemicals causes them to break down into molecules. Scientists then join these molecules into chains. These chains make up plastics. Different combinations of molecules form different kinds of plastic.

HEATING AND MOLDING

Plastics can be made into almost any shape by heating them at a high temperature. The heat softens the plastic, which can then be poured into a mold. As the softened plastic cools, it hardens. When reheated, some types of plastic will soften again. The plastic can then be made into new shapes. Other types of plastic will stay hard even when reheated.

FOUR FAST FACTS

1 In 1869 John Wesley Hyatt, a U.S. inventor, made the first plastic. He called it celluloid because he made it from a plant material called cellulose.

2 In 1909 a U.S. chemist named Leo H. Baekeland developed the first plastic made completely from synthetic (human-made) materials. Baekeland named the new material Bakelite.

3 Plastics are very useful, but they can also cause many problems for the environment. Items made out of plastic do not break down.

4 Recycled plastic can be turned into clothing, outdoor furniture, playground equipment, and more bottles.

This Belgian stamp shows Leo Baekeland.

Bottles at a recycling plant

COMPUTERS

Generally, a computer is any device that can perform numerical calculations—even an adding machine, an abacus, or a slide rule. Currently, however, the term usually refers to an electronic device that can perform automatically a series of tasks according to a precise set of instructions. The set of instructions is called a program, and the tasks may include making arithmetic calculations, storing, retrieving, and processing data, controlling another device, or interacting with a person to perform a business function or to play a game.

Motherboard.

A USB drive stores files so they can be transferred from one device to another.

HARDWARE AND SOFTWARE

A working computer requires both hardware and software. Hardware is the computer's physical electronic and mechanical parts. Software consists of the programs that instruct the hardware to perform tasks.

HARDWARE

A digital computer's hardware is a complex system of four functionally different elements—a central processing unit, input devices, memory-storage devices, and output devices—linked by a communication network, or bus. The bus is usually incorporated into the main circuit board, called the motherboard, which is plugged into all the other components.

The heart of a computer is the central processing unit (CPU). In addition to performing arithmetic and logic operations on data, it times and controls the rest of the system.

This computer comes from the 1980s.

SOFTWARE

Two types of software instruct a computer to perform its tasks—systems software and applications software. Systems software is a permanent component of the computer that controls its fundamental functions. Different kinds of applications software are loaded into the computer as needed to perform specific tasks for the user, such as word processing. Applications software requires the functions provided by the systems software.

THE INTERNET

A large, international computer network, the Internet links tens of millions of users around the world. It is used daily by many individuals for such purposes as sending and receiving e-mail, obtaining mountains of information on almost any subject, social networking, buying and selling products, playing movies and music, and sharing videos and photos. The Internet allows people at far-flung locations to communicate and work collaboratively. It supports access to digital information by many applications, including the World Wide Web.

INTERNET ADDRESSES

An Internet address is needed to receive a message or to send a message to another Internet user. Such addresses have a specific format that indicates the name of the user, the machine they are working on, and where that machine is located.

URLS

Every resource on the Internet also has its own address, called a URL (uniform resource locator)—for example, http://www.britannica.com/biography/William-Shakespeare. The first part of the URL specifies what protocol, or rules, are used to access the resource. In this case "http" indicates that the file is a Web page that uses HyperText Transfer Protocol. The next part of the URL is the domain name, which is the unique online address of an organization or other entity, in this case "www.britannica.com." Finally, the URL may indicate the location of a specific file.

People can use the Internet to communicate with video chats.

ARPANET

The U.S. Department of Defense's now-defunct ARPANET, a network that once linked together universities and research institutions engaged in defense work, was the basis on which the Internet was developed. ARPANET was established in 1969.

WI-FI

The wireless networking technology known as Wi-Fi (wireless fidelity) uses radio waves to transmit data at high speeds over short distances. Wi-Fi is often used in local area networks (LANs), computer networks that link computers and devices over small geographic areas. Because Wi-Fi allows LANs to operate without cables and wiring, it has become a popular choice for home and business networks.

HOTSPOTS

Wi-Fi can be used to provide wireless broadband Internet access for devices such as laptops, smartphones and other cell phones, e-readers, and electronic gaming consoles. Wireless-enabled devices are able to connect to the Internet when they are near areas that have Wi-Fi access, called "hot spots." Hot spots have become common, with many public places such as airports, hotels, bookstores, and coffee shops offering Wi-Fi access. A version of Wi-Fi called Wi-Fi Direct allows connectivity between devices without a LAN.

SMARTPHONES

The multipurpose device known as a smartphone consists of a handheld computer integrated with a mobile phone. It allows the user to browse the Web, send and receive e-mail, view audio and video files, play games, read e-books, and access other computer applications, as well as to make phone calls. Many smartphones also have a built-in camera for recording and transmitting photographs and short videos.

THE FIRST SMARTPHONES

The first smartphone was designed by IBM and sold by BellSouth in 1993. It included a touch-screen interface for accessing its calendar, address book, calculator, and other functions. As the market matured over the following decade, solid-state computer memory and integrated circuits became less expensive. Smartphones became more computer-like, and more-advanced services, such as Internet access via wireless networks, became possible.

TEST WHAT YOU KNOW

1. **How many elements exist in nature?**

   75   94   102

2. **Most of an atom consists of this.**

   Protons   Electrons

   Neutrons   Empty space

3. **Another word for stored energy is kinetic energy.**

   True   False

4. **Even ice cubes have thermal energy.**

   True   False

5. **A chemical reaction is a process by which a substance changes its state of matter. For example, a solid becoming a liquid is a chemical reaction.**

   True   False

6. **Fire needs this element to start.**

   Oxygen   Carbon

7. **Electrical forces are at work in our bodies.**

   True   False

8. **Which telescopes are more powerful?**

   Reflecting telescopes   Refracting telescopes

9. **Can a human be scanned by an electron microscope?**

   Yes   No

10. **Thomas Edison invented the first incandescent lamp.**

    True   False

1. 94; 2. Empty space; 3. False; 4. True; 5. False; 6. Oxygen; 7. True; 8. Reflecting telescopes; 9. No; 10. False